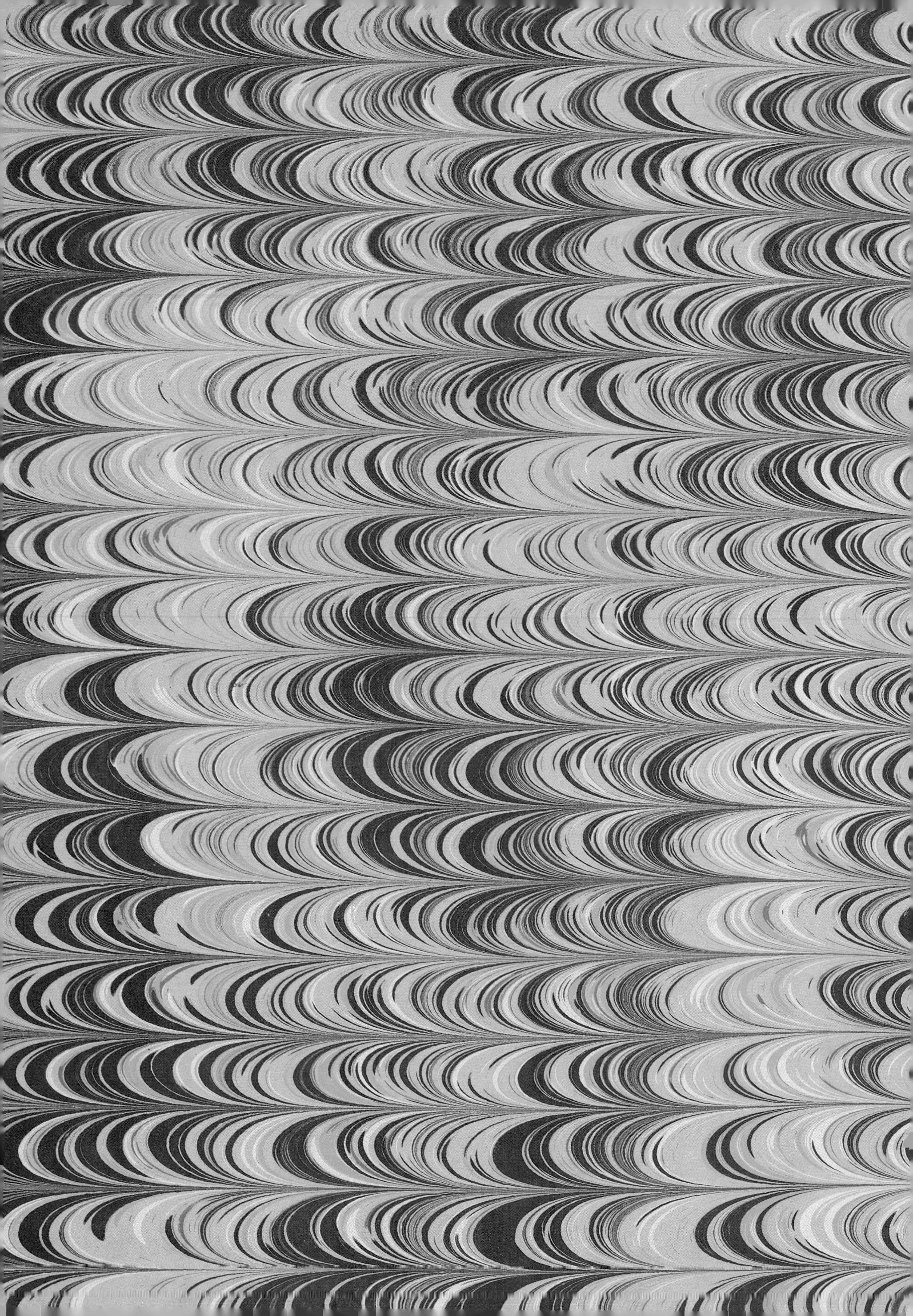

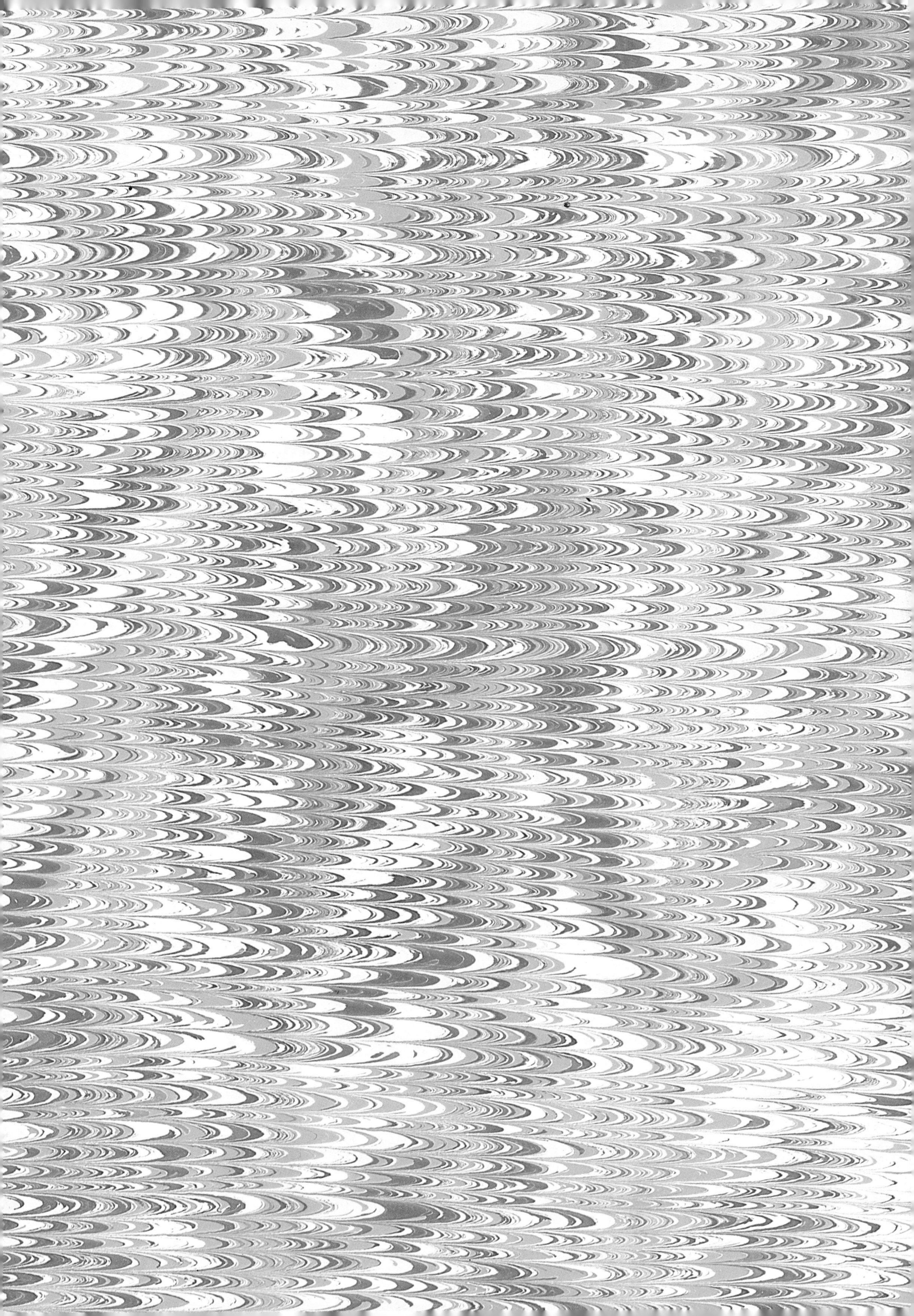

MARBLE TEX
FOR 10% SCRE
ON PICTURE PA

& ALSO USED I
PAGE BORDER
TREATMENT.

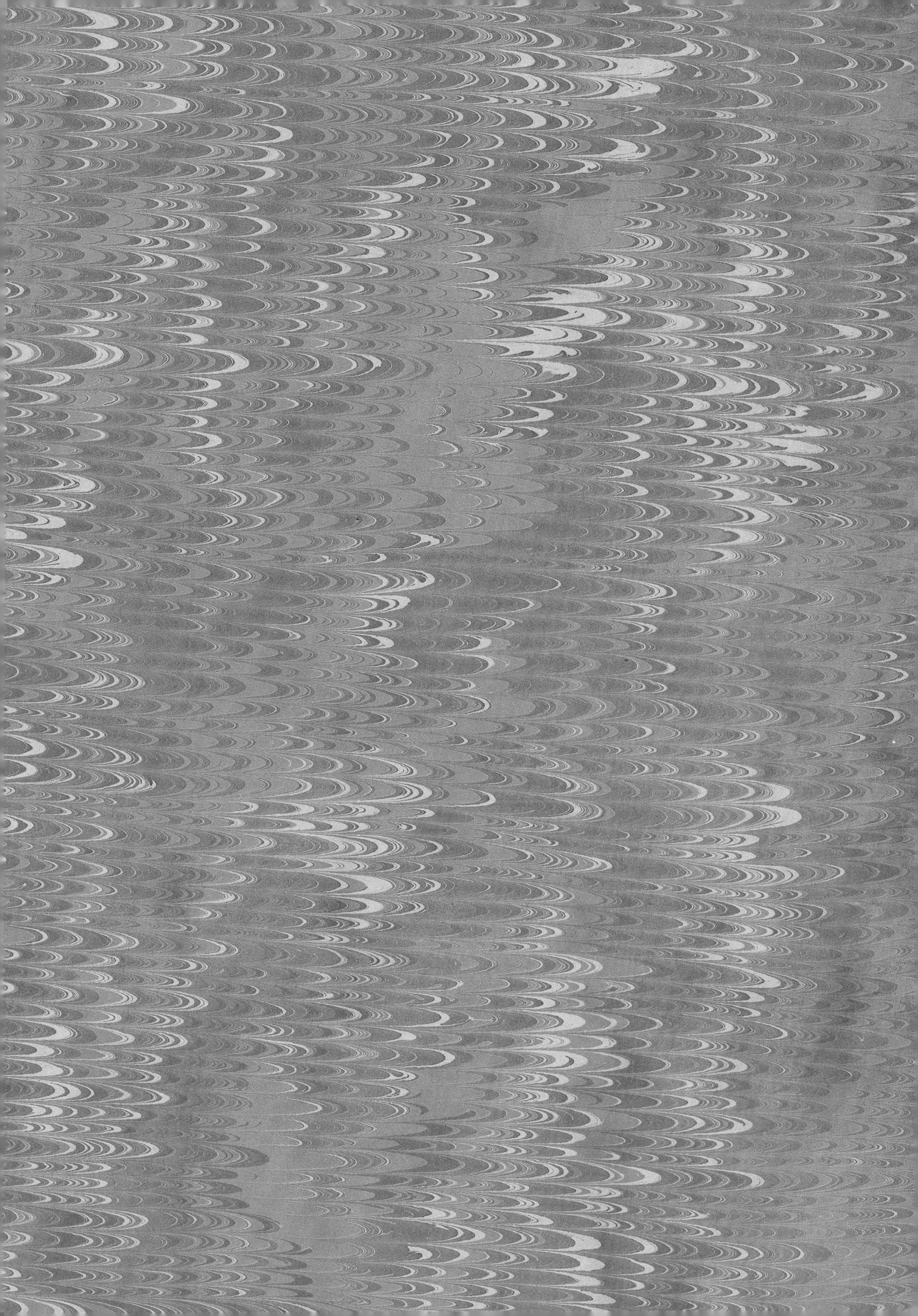

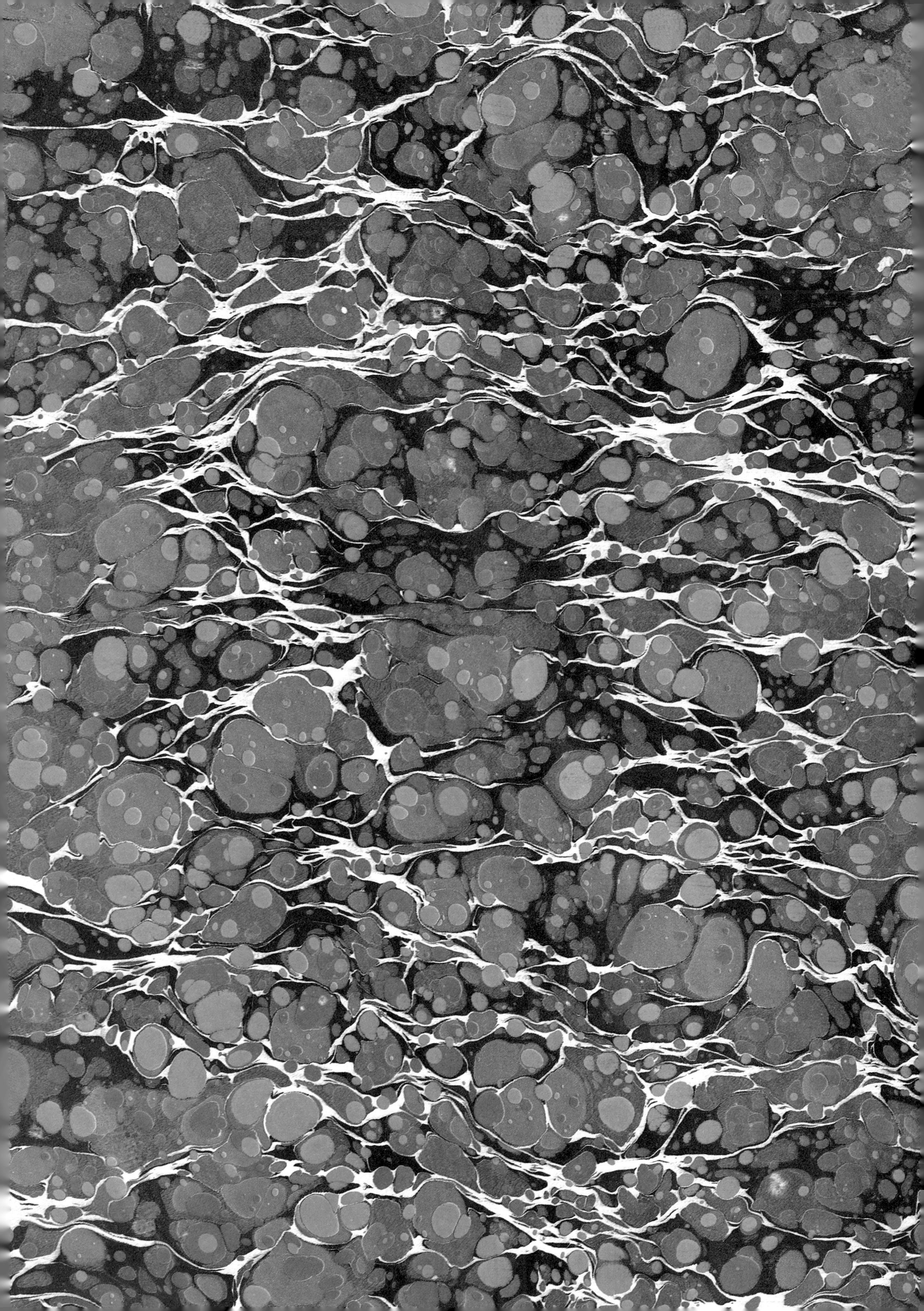

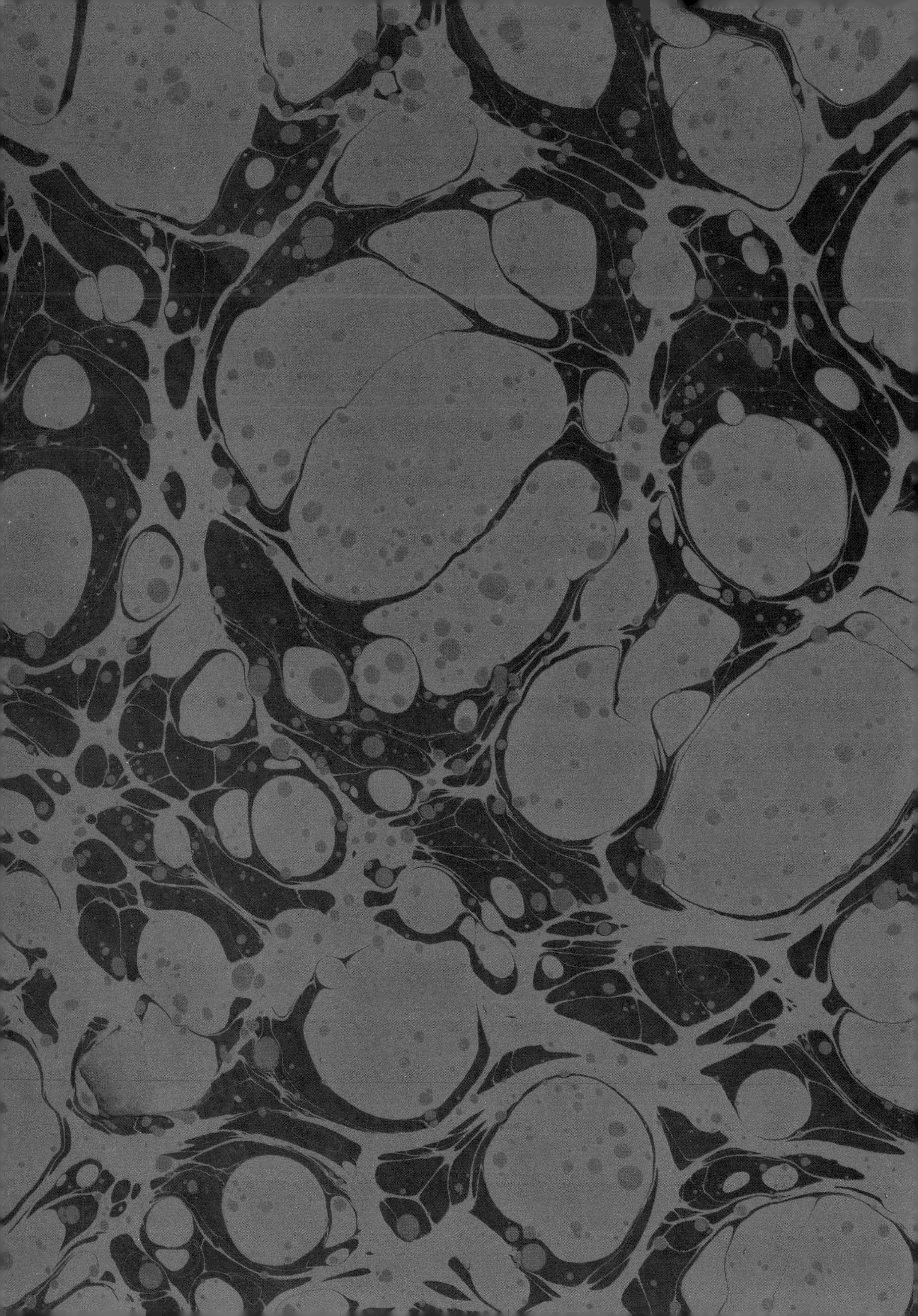

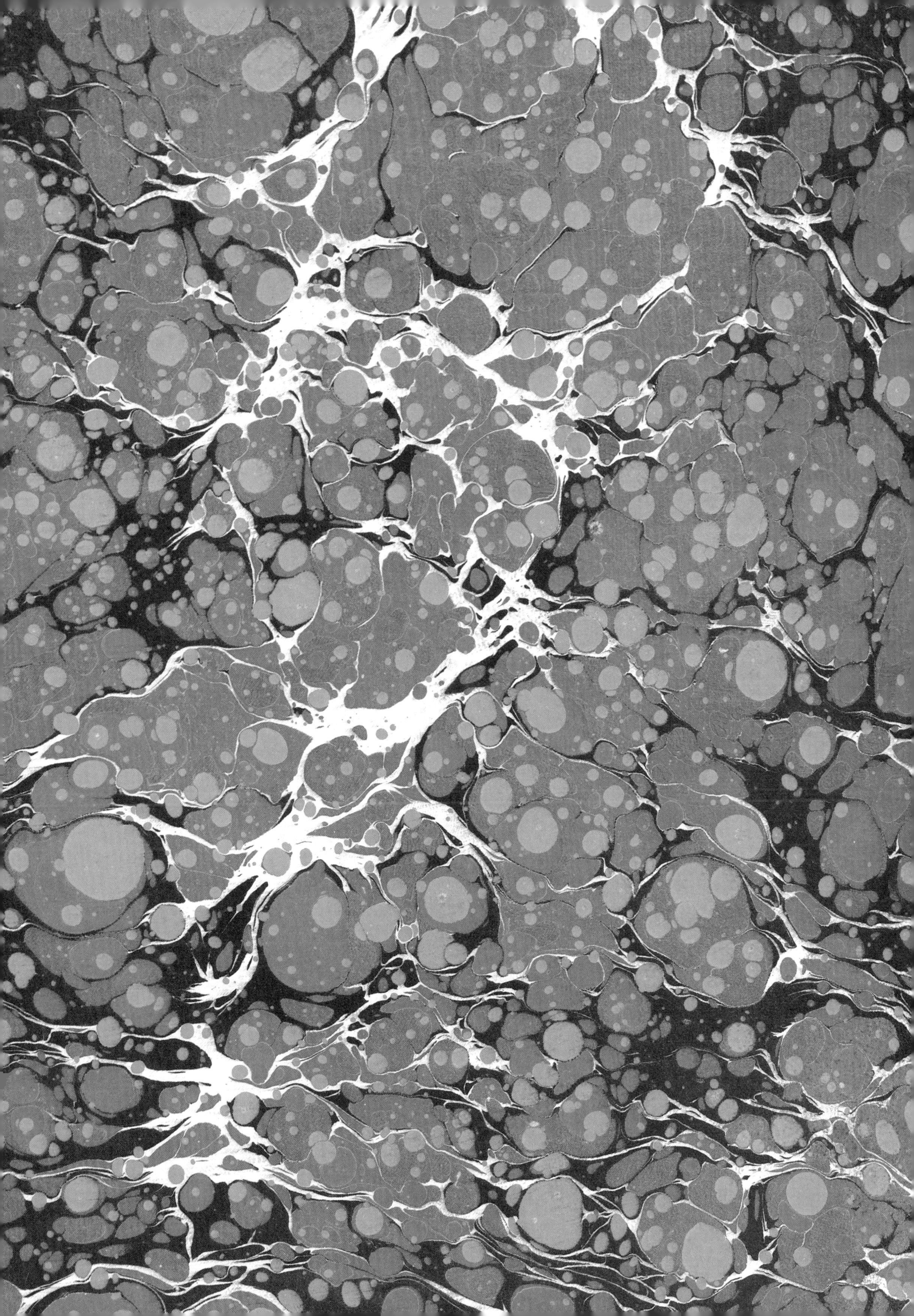

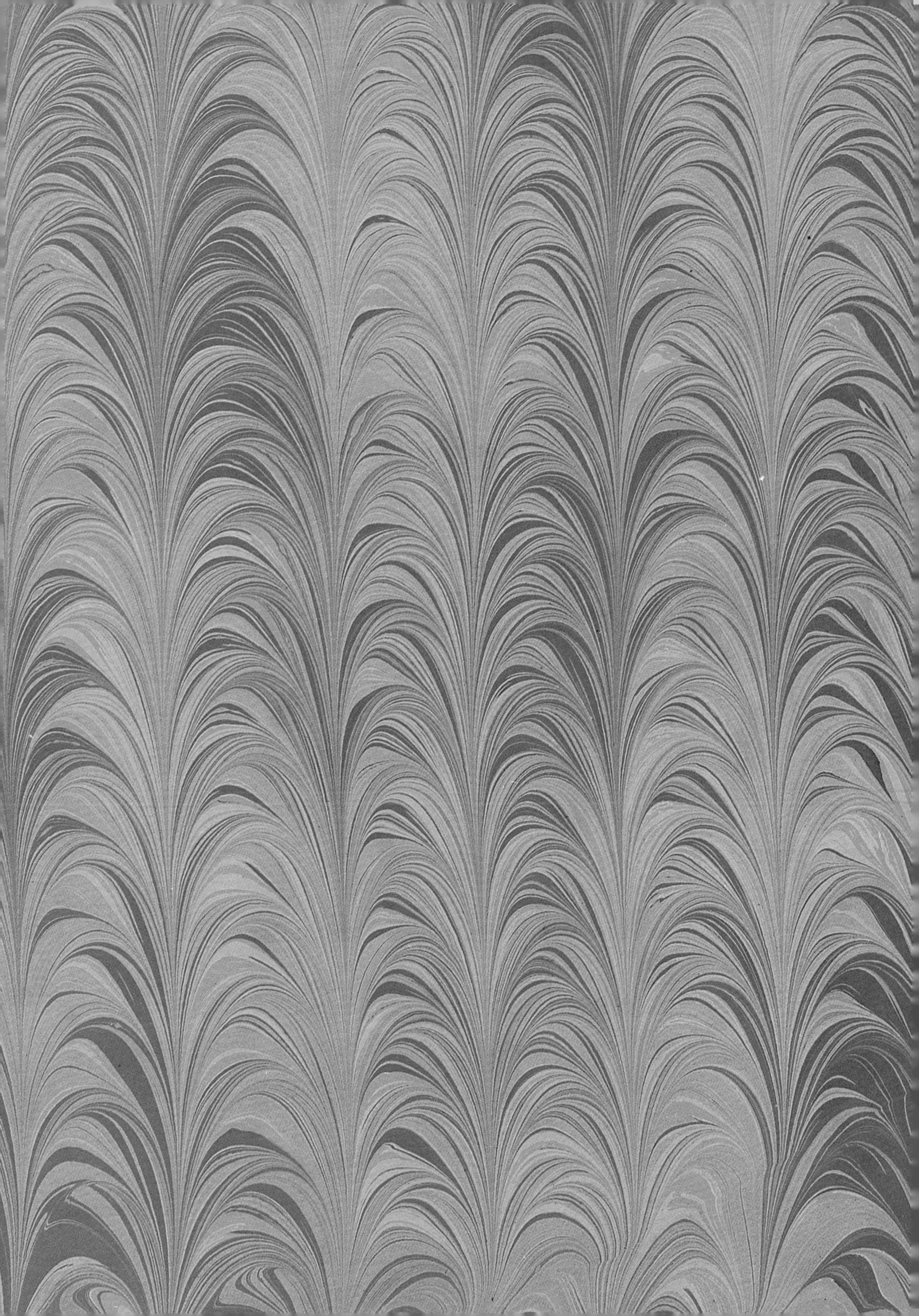

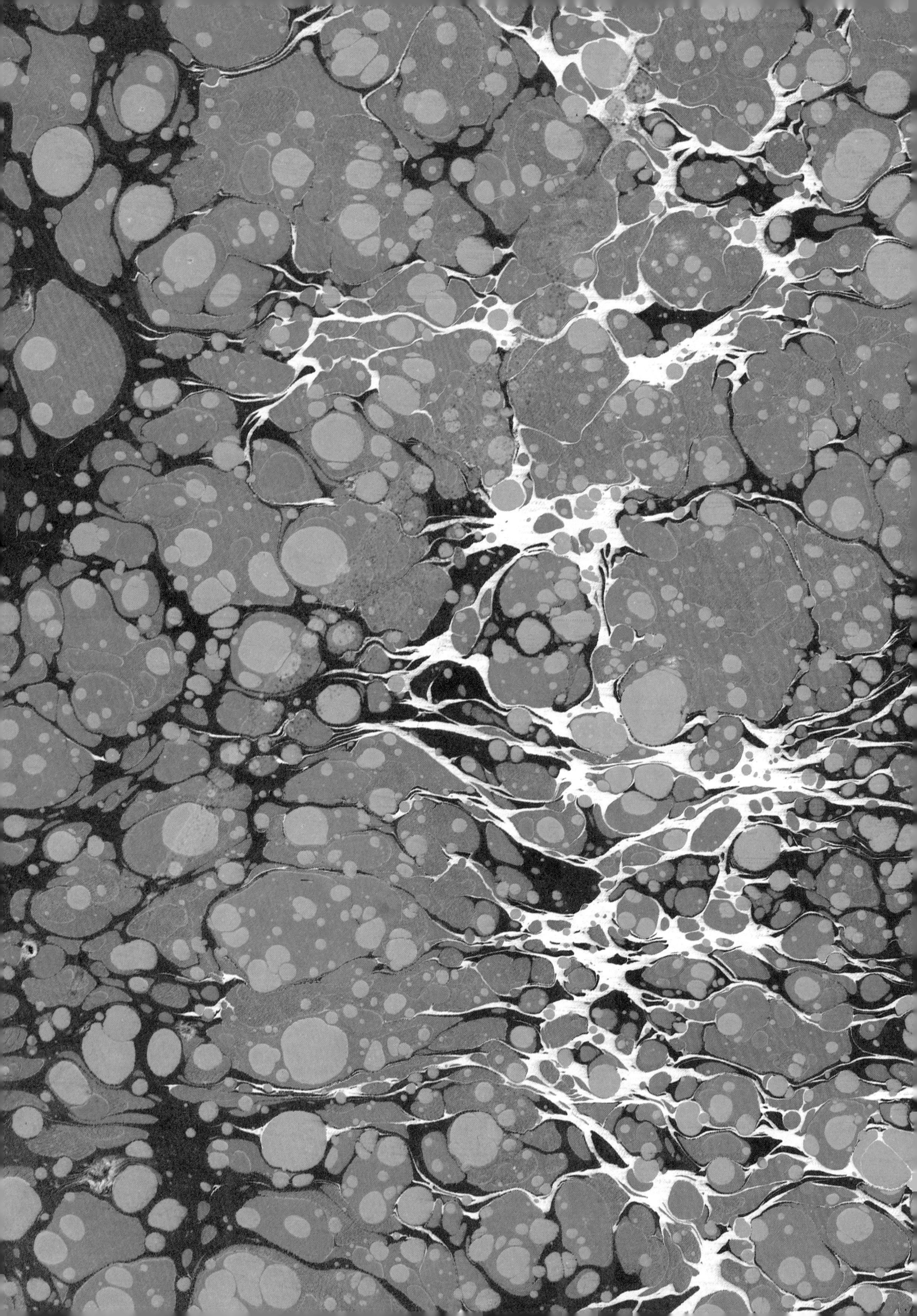

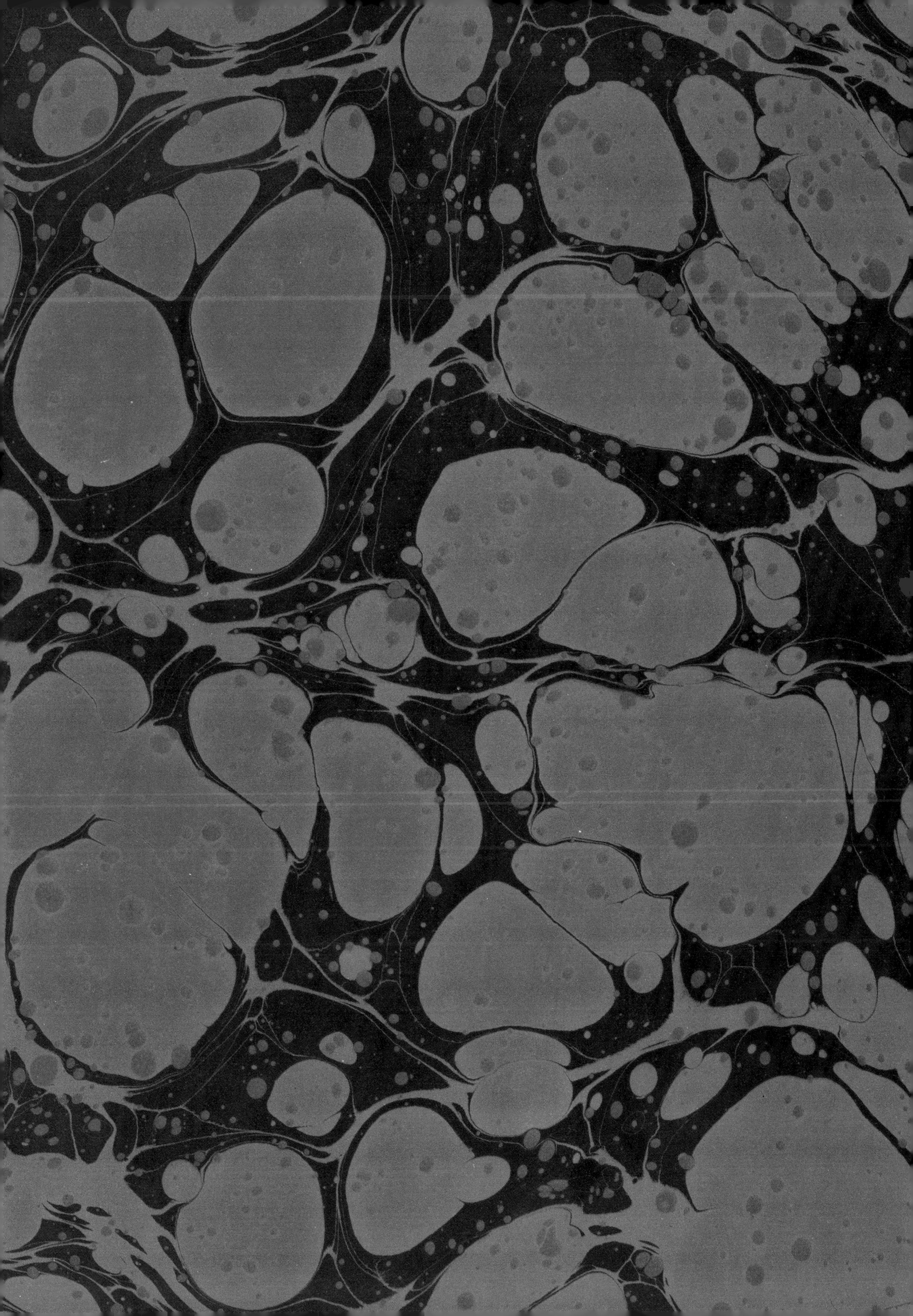

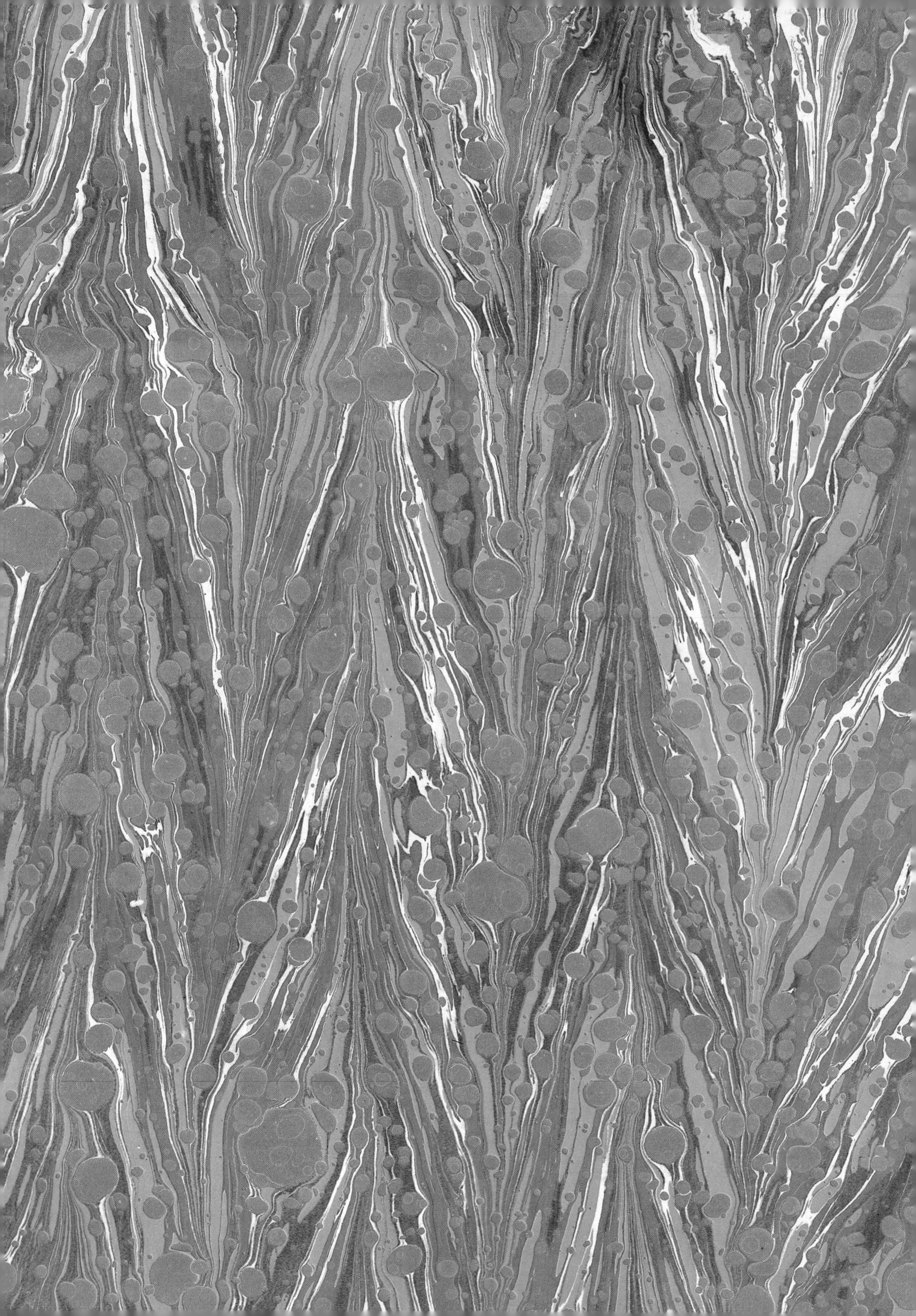

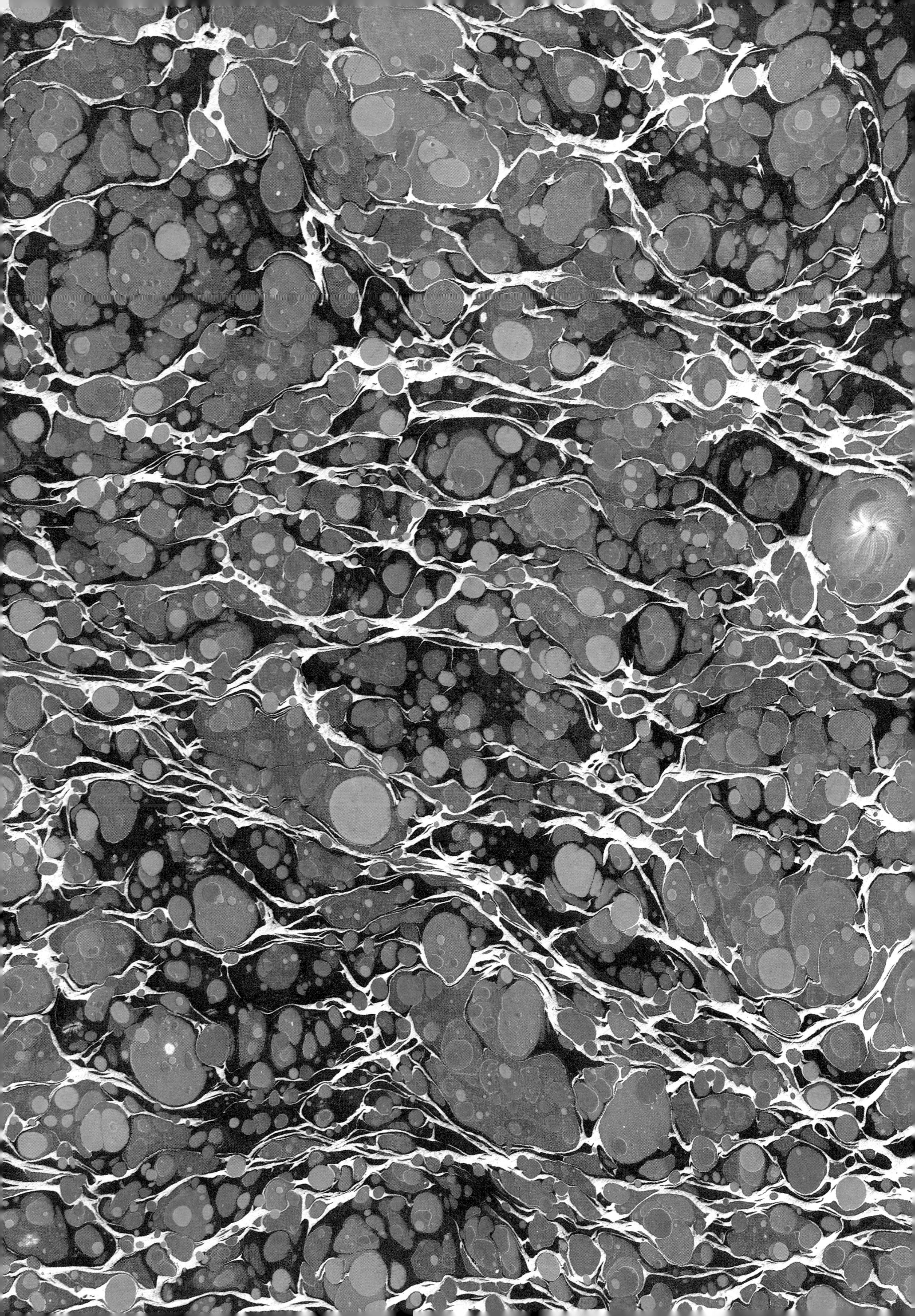

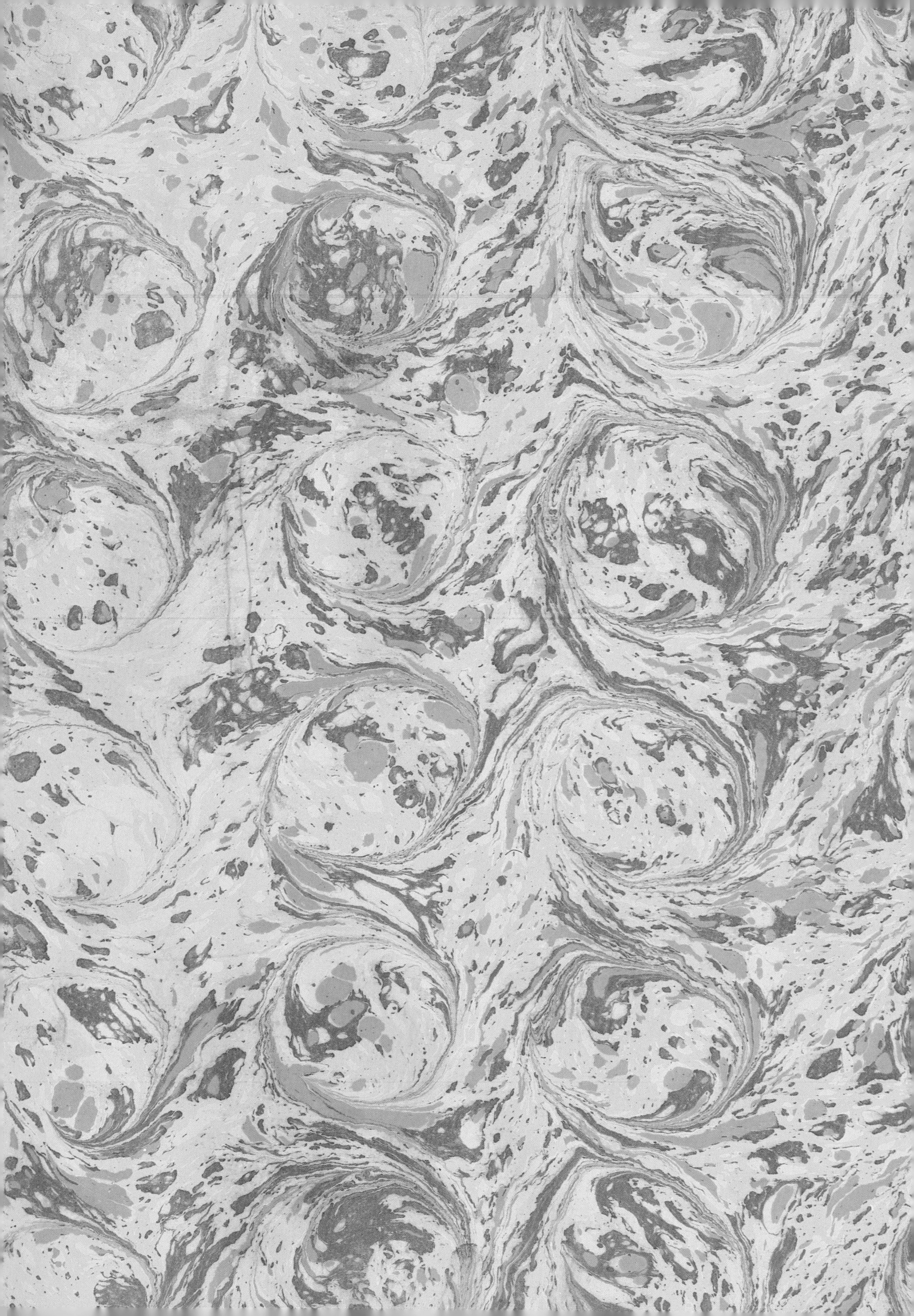

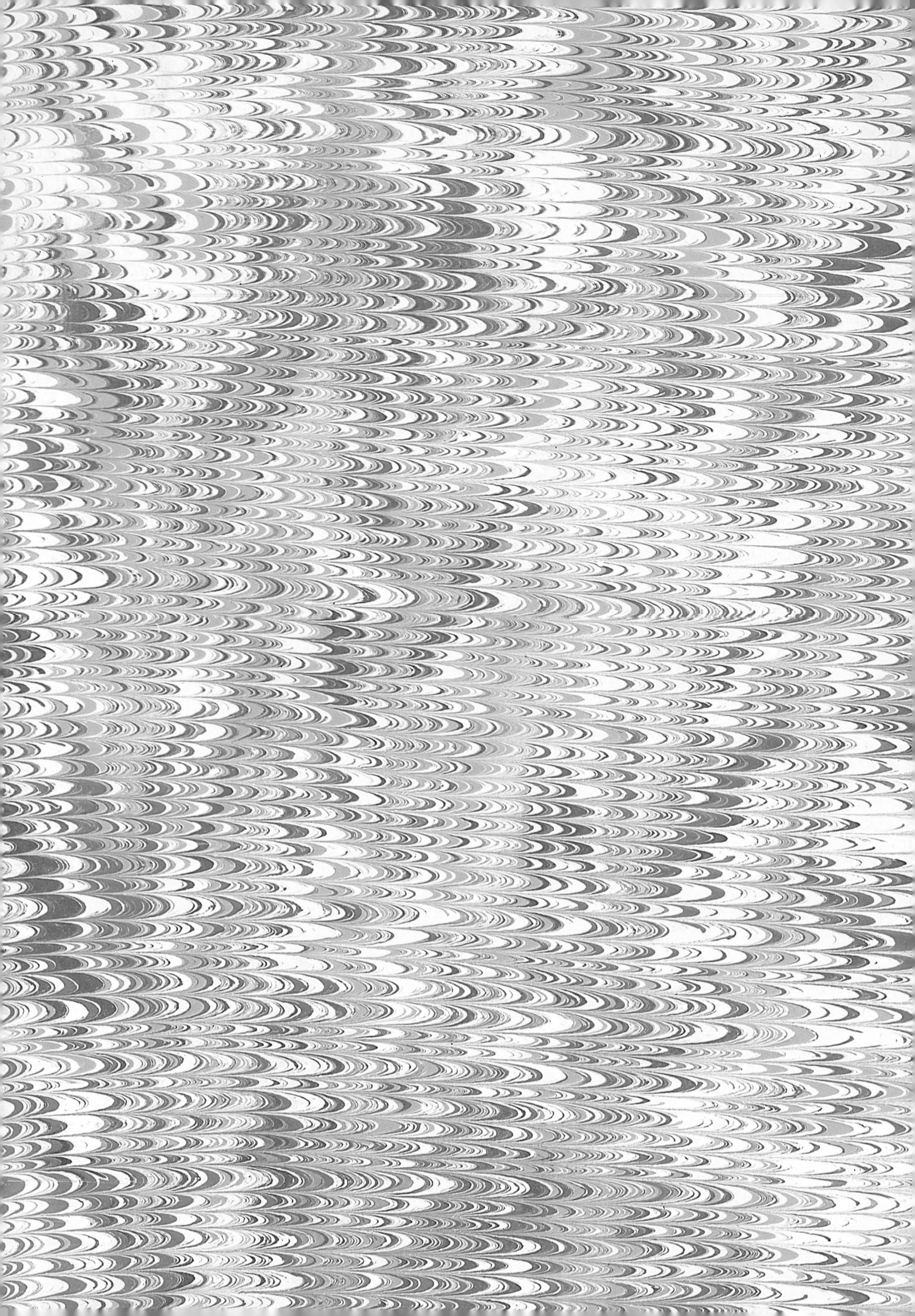

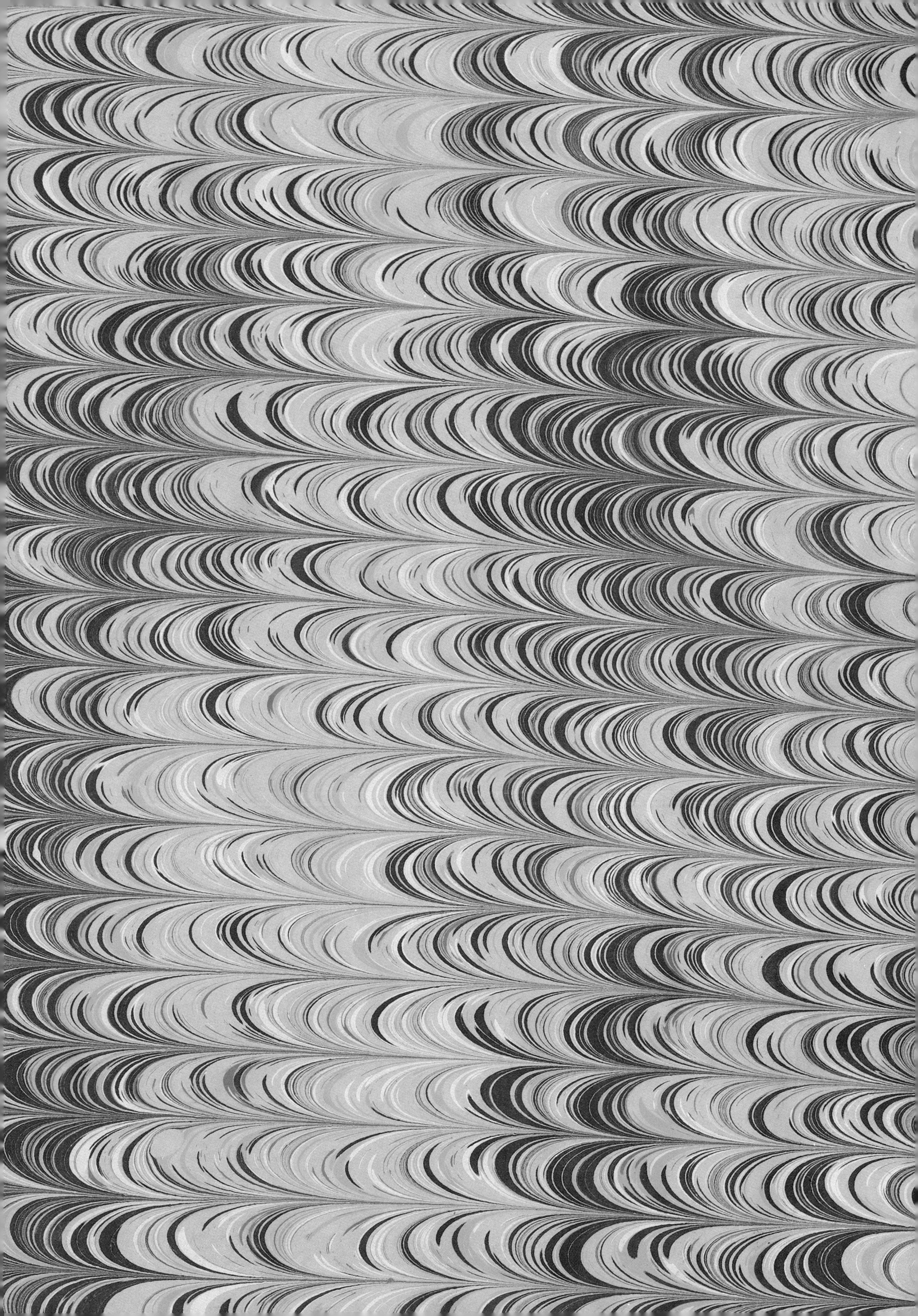